KU-166-045

© 1993 Grandreams Limited

This edition published in 1995.

Published by
Grandreams Limited
Jadwin House, 205/211 Kentish Town Road,
London, NW5 2JU.

Printed in Czech Republic.

FIFTY BEDTIME STORIES

Written by Ann McKie

Illustrated by Ken McKie

CONTENTS

The Little Lost Hedgehog

Mrs Hedgehog had such a large family that she had to wash lots of clothes everyday.

When the weather was warm and breezy, all ten young hedgehogs lent a hand, and the washing was done in next to no time.

"Today is perfect for washing our clothes," said Mrs Hedgehog, as she gave everyone a job. "Two of you scrub the clothes, two of you rinse off the soap suds, two of you wring them dry, two of you hang them on the line, and two tiny ones hand me the pegs!"

Very soon all the dirty clothes were clean and bright and hanging on the clothesline in the sun.

"We all deserve a rest," smiled Mrs Hedgehog. So she sat down on the grassy bank near the clothesline, took off her hat and put it down by her side. All her little hedgehogs sat beside her with glasses of cool lemonade and buttery biscuits.

"How lucky I am," thought Mrs Hedgehog, "to have such helpful children." All of a sudden she gave a squeal. "There are only nine of you! Where is Baby Hedgehog?"

The young hedgehogs put down their lemonade and biscuits and began to search at once. They looked everywhere, in the house, in the garden, in the meadow, in the wood, they even looked in the empty clothes baskets.

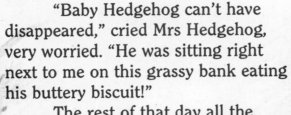

"Baby Hedgehog can't have disappeared," cried Mrs Hedgehog, very worried. "He was sitting right next to me on this grassy bank eating his buttery biscuit!"

The rest of that day all the hedgehogs searched long and hard. The sun began to set behind the hill and soon it would be dark.

"We must have searched everywhere," sighed Mrs Hedgehog as she wiped a tear from her eye. She sat down on the grassy bank near the clothesline and began to cry. Several of the younger hedgehogs began to sniff too.

Poor Mrs Hedgehog bent over to pick up her hat that she had left there since the morning and what do you think she saw?

Baby Hedgehog fast asleep! He must have crawled under his mother's hat and fallen asleep in the sun.

How the young hedgehogs cheered, they were so happy to find Baby Hedgehog. They made such a noise that their woodland friends nearby came out to join in the celebrations.

The Pink Elephant's Party

When Pink Elephant moved to Toy Town she was rather worried. "I hope I shall make new friends quickly," she said, as she unlocked the door to her new home.

At first Pink Elephant was busy settling in. She moved the furniture around until everything was exactly in the right place. Then, she put up brand new curtains, hung her favourite paintings on the walls, and filled all her vases with bunches of summer flowers.

"How lovely everything looks!" sighed Pink Elephant happily, and she sat down to admire her new home.

"It's very quiet in Toy Town," thought Pink Elephant, as she gazed out of the window into the empty street.

"I have an idea," she cried jumping up. "I'll give a party and invite everybody in the street. That way I will soon make friends."

So, there and then, Pink Elephant wrote out a huge pile of party invitations for the next afternoon. Then she ran up and down the street popping an envelope through every letter box.

The rest of the day Pink Elephant tidied her front garden. She mowed the lawn and swept the path. She polished the knocker on the front door and put the numbers back on the gate because they had fallen off.

Next morning, Pink Elephant got up very early and baked all kinds of lovely things to eat. After lunch, she decorated the house with balloons and coloured streamers. Last of all, she put on her party dress and then waited for her guests to arrive.

Pink Elephant waited and waited, but no-one came. She waited until it was past tea-time, but not one single guest arrived.

At last she opened her front door and walked down the garden path to the gate. What a surprise the Pink Elephant got! There were crowds of toys walking past with armfuls of presents and cards.

"Where are you all going?" shouted Pink Elephant, as they walked by.

"To Pink Elephant's party!" cried a furry rabbit as he waved the invitation in the air.

"But the party is here, at my house!" said Pink Elephant. "Why are you all walking past?"

"You live at Number 31," the rabbit answered, "and the invitation says Number 13."

"Oh dear!" gasped Pink Elephant. "I must have put the numbers back on my gate the wrong way round!"

How the toys laughed. They all crowded into Number 13. Pink Elephant gave a wonderful party and made lots of new friends.

Ben's New Seat

Once upon a time, a grizzly bear called Ben made himself a seat.

"I'm rather lonely by myself in the forest," said Ben. "I shall sit here on my seat and see who passes by."

Very soon, along came a grey rabbit who hopped up onto Ben's knee. Then a squirrel jumped down from a branch overhead.

Two racoons who were scampering by, stopped when they saw Ben's seat, then jumped up on either side of him.

"Is there room for us?" asked a red fox and a stoat.

"And us?" squeaked a family of mice.

"It's a bit of a squeeze," shouted Ben. So everyone moved in tight and chattered together all afternoon.

They made such a noise that a tiny bluebird flew across to join in the fun. "Can I perch on your seat please?" the tiny bird asked Ben as he fluttered down.

Sadly, that was too much for Ben's new seat. It creaked and groaned and cracked. One by one the wooden legs snapped and everyone fell onto the ground laughing and giggling.

"Tomorrow I shall make a brand new seat, big enough for all my new friends," chuckled grizzly bear Ben, happily.

Three Jolly Fishermen

Once upon a time three jolly fishermen went to sea in a boat with a bright green sail.

The three jolly fishermen loved music and as they fished they sang. When the sea was calm and still, they sang quiet lullabies. When the boat bobbed up and down on the waves they sang jolly songs together. But when stormy winds blew and great waves crashed over their tiny boat, they sang opera as loud as they could.

Everyday the three jolly fisherman went out in their boat with the bright green sail, but they never ever caught a fish.

And this is the reason why!

The three jolly fisherman made such a noise that all the fish could hear them. As soon as they began to sing, every fish in the bay would gather under the boat with the bright green sail and sing along. The lobsters and crabs, all the fish and huge whales, joined a choir under the sea.

They were so busy singing together and learning new songs, they never ever got caught. And so none of them ended up on a plate for tea!

The Little Green Tractor

The little green tractor was very pleased with himself. All year long he had been working very hard helping the farmer. In spring he had pulled the plough and in summer he had taken all the hay back to the farm in his trailer. At harvest time he had carried so many loads of corn that all the farmer's barns were full for the winter.

"I think I shall go on holiday now!" said the little green tractor to the farmer. "I've worked very hard all year and I need a change!"

The farmer looked very puzzled. He had never heard of a tractor going on holiday before.

So early the next morning the little green tractor drove out of the farmyard, down the lane then turned left on to the main highway.

At first the road was quiet and the little green tractor chugged along happily. A few cars and vans drove past him and one or two lorry drivers waved as they went by.

On and on went the little green tractor until he came to a busy town. Here the road was filled with traffic and everyone was travelling very fast.

All of a sudden the cars, buses and trucks screeched to a halt at the traffic lights. But the little green tractor just carried on. (He had never seen a red light before, and didn't know he must stop!)

What a noise the other traffic made. They blew their horns so loudly at the little green tractor that he almost crashed.

As soon as he could, the frightened little green tractor turned off the main road into a garage and came to a stop.

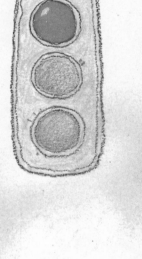

15

"How I wish I was back home on the farm," said the little green tractor. "Now I shall never get home!"

As soon as the garage owner saw the little green tractor he was puzzled. "What on earth are you doing here?" he asked. "Have you lost your way?"

The little green tractor didn't know what to say.

"Our driver is taking a tanker full of fuel to your farm in five minutes. He'll give you a tow."

So that is how the little green tractor got safely back to the farm.

That night the farmer filled the little green tractor up with fuel and checked his engine. Then he gave the paintwork a polish until it shone.

Nothing was said about tractors going on holiday ever again!

The Bucket With A Hole

A small girl called Jane spent a week by the sea. She had a wonderful time. The weather was fine and the sea was warm and clear. Jane loved to carry water from the sea in her bright red bucket and then pour it into a deep hole she made with her spade. It was great fun!

On the very last day of her holiday, Jane found a hole in her bucket, then she noticed that the handle was loose.

"My bucket's no good any more!" said Jane sadly as she left it on the beach and went home.

"That's the end of me," said the bright red bucket as he lay forgotten on the sand.

A crab came over to try and cheer him up. "Something is bound to turn up," said the crab kindly, but still the bucket felt very miserable.

After a few days, a little boy came running across the beach. He saw the bright red bucket, but didn't mind that it had a hole and a broken handle. He shouted, "You're just what I need!" and picked up the bucket straight away.

The bucket and the little boy stayed together all summer long and when the little boy went home he took the bucket with him!

Archie Goes Visiting

Archie, the polar bear, lived in the Arctic, quite close to the North Pole. He didn't mind the freezing cold or the bitter winds at all because he had a coat of thick white fur to keep him warm. Archie could go for a swim in the ice-cold sea, then sit down on the ice and he didn't even shiver.

"I love living in the Arctic," said Archie, "except for one thing!"

"What's that then?" asked a Walrus, who had just scrambled up onto the ice.

"I have such a long way to walk to visit my polar bear friends!" said Archie with a sigh.

"How about going by air?" asked the Walrus, as he pointed to an aircraft that had just landed on the ice.

"I'm far too big to fit into one of those!" the polar bear laughed. "It would never take off!"

Just then, a team of huskies sped past pulling a sled. "Stop a minute!" yelled Archie, as he ran after them. "Can you give me a lift?" but the dogs just stuck out their tongues and ran even faster.

"I suppose I shall have to walk all the way as usual," sighed Archie, as he set off across the ice to visit his friends.

All of a sudden, something whizzed past him and pulled up at the explorers' camp over the hill.

"A snow mobile!" yelled Archie. "That's just what I need!"

The explorers were quite surprised when a polar bear knocked at their door. Archie asked in such a polite voice to borrow their snow mobile, they just couldn't refuse.

So if you ever visit the frozen lands quite close to the North Pole, and if you should happen to spot a polar bear whizzing across the ice on a snow mobile, it's likely to be Archie visiting his friends!

The Flying Mail

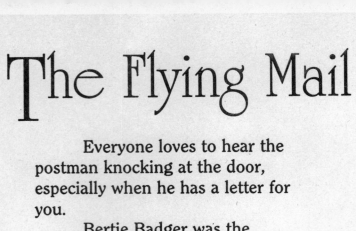

Everyone loves to hear the postman knocking at the door, especially when he has a letter for you.

Bertie Badger was the woodland postman. He had to walk a very long way to deliver his letters to houses all over the wood.

One day as he was sitting on a log having a rest and a cup of tea, a pigeon flew down to join him.

"Would you like some help?" he cooed.

Postman Badger laughed and gave the pigeon some of his sandwich. "You're a bit too small to be a postman."

Off flew the pigeon and very soon came back with some of his friends. When they saw Bertie Badger's sack they set to work straight away.

The smaller birds sorted the mail while the bigger birds carried the parcels between them.

Postman Badger watched in amazement. The birds came everyday to help deliver the mail on time and Postman Badger made extra sandwiches for them all - just to say thank you.

Texas Grandpa's Jeep

One day Texas Grandpa noticed that his Jeep had a flat front tyre. His grandson Pete went to the garage and pumped it up with the air hose.

Texas Grandpa talked so much that Pete forgot to switch off the hose. Now look at the tyre!

"Grandson Pete," shouted Texas Grandpa. "Pump up the other three!"

Now look at the jeep!

"That's just dandy!" yelled Texas Grandpa as he threw his hat high in the air.

"I've always wanted big wheels!"

Ordinary Street

Down Ordinary Street lived Mr Black. Mrs Grey lived just next door. Mr Brown lived on the other side, but the house next door to him was empty. No-one had lived there for a long time and the house had nothing inside.

One day Mrs White came to buy the house. "Oh dear! I couldn't live here!" she cried. "It's dusty and full of cobwebs." So she went away.

Next Mr Green came to look at the house. "The garden is far too small. There is no room for all my plants!" And he marched off down the street.

The following day Mrs Yellow arrived to look inside. "My goodness," she gasped, "it's far too dark. I need sunshine in every room!" And she drove off in her open car.

Now one dark day, when Ordinary Street was wet with rain, a truck full of noisy children came screeching round the corner.

Suddenly the rain clouds blew away, a patch of blue appeared in the sky and the sun shone brightly.

"We are the Rainbows," called the family to Mr Black, Mrs Grey and Mr Brown who were watching from their front doors.

"What a wonderful house!" gasped Mr and Mrs Rainbow and all the Rainbow children. I think we shall stay here for ever." And they did!

They painted the house in bright colours and filled the garden with beautiful flowers.

"I think," said Mr Black to Mr Grey. "we ought to do the same."

"I agree," nodded Mr Brown. So they started at once.

Soon the street looked so different that it didn't seem ordinary any more.

"Let's call it Bright Street." So they changed the name right away!

23

Mr Maggs And Monty

Little Mr Maggs had a big dog named Monty who loved to go for very long walks. Monty's legs were so long that little Mr Maggs had to run to keep up with him.

Every morning after breakfast, Monty would wait by the front door for little Mr Maggs to put on his hat and coat and take him out again.

They would walk all afternoon and come back home just in time for tea. Then after a quick snooze in front of the fire, Monty was ready to go out again.

Sometimes it was almost dark when they returned. Then little Mr Maggs would hang up Monty's lead and go straight to bed, quite tired out.

One morning after breakfast Monty went to the back door as usual, waiting to go for a walk. But little Mr Maggs put on his hat and coat and went out leaving Monty at home.

Little Mr Maggs hurried to the shops and came back with a mysterious parcel.

After lunch as usual, little Mr Maggs put on his hat and coat and put Monty's lead on him.

Soon they were both whizzing along. Monty ran faster and faster, but still Mr Maggs kept up. Monty couldn't understand why!

At last poor Monty had to stop for a rest and when he looked round, he saw that little Mr Maggs was wearing ROLLER SKATES!

That is what was in the mysterious parcel.

24

Tom and Peter bought two big balloons. Tom's balloon was red and Peter's balloon was blue.

The next day as Tom was looking out of his bedroom window, he saw a big blue balloon.

The Big Blue Balloon

"That must be Peter!" laughed naughty Tom. "I'll burst his big blue balloon!" So, very quietly, Tom opened the window, and using a sharp pin he burst the big blue balloon. It went off with a very loud bang.

That made Tom laugh even more. Straight away there was a loud knocking on Tom's door. He ran downstairs at once, and from behind the front door a very big voice boomed, "Who burst my big blue balloon?"

Now Tom had some quick thinking to do!

25

What A Strange House!

"What a lovely morning," said Lottie, as she opened the front door. "I think I shall go for a ride on my bike." So she ran upstairs to find her shorts.

When she opened the shed door, Lottie got quite a surprise. "Someone has been very busy in here!" she cried, then ran outside to find her grandad.

Two blackbirds had built a nest in the basket on the front of her bike. "No more bike rides for you for a while!" chuckled Grandad.

"What a strange house for blackbirds," giggled Lottie. "I'll go for a walk and see what else I can find."

When Lottie called at the cottage down the lane, she found that two swallows had built a nest in the front porch. Everyone would have to use the back door for a few weeks.

Later she called at the farm on the hill and she saw a duck sitting on six eggs. Lottie could hardly believe her eyes, the nest was on the farmer's old tractor seat!

Next she met her friend from school who had just found a robin's nest in a plant pot.

Then a lady called her over to see some mice nesting in a garden chair.

"What strange houses I've seen today!" said Lottie as she ran past the mill.

"Come in and see our new kittens, they've made their home in a barrel," shouted the miller's wife.

Lottie rushed inside and bent down to find six tiny kittens fast asleep in an old flour barrel.

"I have a surprise for you Lottie," whispered the miller's wife in her ear. "Your grandad has asked you to choose two kittens for your very own, and take them back home today!"

How carefully Lottie walked back home, with her two kittens tucked up in a shopping basket.

Her grandad was smiling as he opened the back door. "Now where are you going to keep those Lottie?"

As soon as she put the basket on the floor, both kittens jumped out and ran straight into Lottie's dolls' house.

"What a strange house for two kittens," laughed Lottie. "Welcome to your new home!"

As for the kittens, they were already fast asleep.

The Lonely Monkey

Far away across a bright blue ocean was a tiny desert island. Everyday the sun shone down on the sandy beach and warmed the clear waters around the shore.

In the middle of this island grew tall palm trees full of coconuts and banana plants loaded with bunches of ripe bananas.

And who do you think lived in this wonderful place? Just one little brown monkey with a curly tail.

"I'm so lonely, I wish I had a friend!" said the monkey out loud as he sat on the beach. But he knew there was no-one to hear him.

A brilliant coloured fish swimming by, stuck his head out of the water. "Follow me and swim to the next island. It's full of little brown 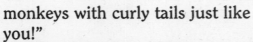 monkeys with curly tails just like you!"

"But I can't swim," cried the monkey. "Please fish, will you teach me how?"

"Certainly!" replied the fish. "Just walk into the water and do as I say."

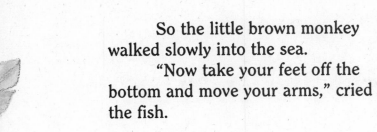

So the little brown monkey walked slowly into the sea.

"Now take your feet off the bottom and move your arms," cried the fish.

"Oh dear!" shrieked the monkey. "I don't like this one bit! Swimming is far too wet."

The brightly coloured fish just laughed and swam away, while the monkey dried on the sand.

Now standing on the beach was a great white pelican. "Come with me and fly to the island. I'm taking off right now!"

"But I can't fly," cried the monkey. "Please pelican, will you teach me how?"

"Certainly!" replied the pelican. "Climb on top of the tallest palm tree, flap your arms and fly away!"

The monkey did as the pelican had said, but he fell with a thud onto the sand, and some of the coconuts fell on top of him. When he looked up the pelican had flown away.

All of a sudden the little monkey leapt to his feet. "I know!" he shouted out loud. "I'll chop down the coconut trees and the huge banana plants and make a raft." He jumped up and down with glee. "I shall sail across to the other island and make friends with the other monkeys."

"What a very silly idea," said a voice from the sea. The little brown monkey looked up to see a small turtle walking slowly up the beach. "Chop down all the

trees and you'll have nothing to eat and neither will anyone else."

The monkey hung his head. "I don't have an axe!" he muttered.

"Just as well!" the turtle said, shaking his head. "I could take you across to the island on my back, but you're far too big." And with that the

small green turtle walked slowly back into the sea.

This made the little brown monkey feel so sad and lonely, that he sat on the sand and cried.

Then all of a sudden, out of the sea, rose the biggest turtle you have ever seen. Very slowly he plodded towards the sad little brown monkey.

"Dry those tears, climb onto my back and don't forget to hold on tight," said the big turtle with a smile. "You'll never be lonely again when we reach the other island."

The turtle's shell looked so

large, the little monkey knew he would be quite safe.

When the little brown monkey looked down into the clear blue sea, what do you think he saw? Bobbing up and down in the water next to them was the little green turtle.

"I knew I was far too small to carry you to the island, so I asked my great great grandfather to help you. He's very kind and very wise."

"So are you," said the monkey with a smile. "Thank you for everything, little green turtle. I shall never be lonely again."

A Shelf Full Of Dolls

Sarah's daddy had a job at the airport. Most of the time he went to work in the morning and came home every night. But sometimes he flew away to different countries and stayed there for a few days.

Every time he came back from a trip abroad, Sarah's daddy brought her a doll. She had a different doll from every country he visited!

Sarah's daddy had put up some shelves on Sarah's bedroom wall so that she could look at her collection of dolls all the time. One day he added a new shelf next to the others.

"All ready for the new doll I'll be bringing back from my next trip!" he said.

"It's a very long shelf for one doll!" said Sarah, looking puzzled as she waved her daddy goodbye.

After a week, Daddy returned and brought Sarah the new doll he had promised. And what a strange doll it was. It had no arms or legs, it was made of painted wood and rattled!

"This is a Russian doll," Daddy smiled, as he unscrewed its body and found another doll inside.

Then Sarah unscrewed the second doll and found another. On and on she went until there were nine beautiful Russian dolls, each one a little bit smaller than the other.

"Now I know why you put up such a long shelf!" laughed Sarah, as she placed the dolls in a row.

The Professor's Pencil

Jack lived next door to Professor Smart, who spent all day and most of the night inventing things!

"I wish you could invent something to help me," said Jack with a grin, as he sat outside on the step practising his handwriting in an exercise book.

"I most certainly can!" replied the Professor, and he rushed off to start work straight away.

All that day and most of the next, Jack could hear rattling and banging coming from next door.

"Finished at last!" cried the Professor from over the fence. Jack jumped up at once and ran round to his house to take a look. There in the garden was the strangest machine Jack had ever seen.

"What is that?" asked Jack in amazement.

"A machine for making full stops!" said the Professor with pride.

Jack laughed until he cried. "But I can do that easily with one small pencil."

"Oh dear!" sighed the Professor. "Of course you can, what a silly man I am!"

"Never mind," said Jack smiling, "your machine will be perfect for planting Dad's seeds!"

32

Ossie's Umbrella

Every morning Ossie the ostrich went for a run across the plain. Now, as you know, ostriches can run very fast indeed, but they cannot fly.

Ossie really wanted to fly. "If I run fast enough, one day I may take off and fly up into the air," he thought. Sad to say, he never did!

One fine morning, after a long hard run, Ossie the ostrich stopped for a rest. As he looked down on the ground he spotted a brightly coloured snake.

"Lovely morning for a run!" giggled Ossie, because he knew that snakes never ran anywhere.

When the snake didn't reply, Ossie felt a bit ashamed. "I was only teasing," he said as he bent down to the snake. "Sorry."

Suddenly Ossie heard loud laughter, it was a little rhino who had stopped to see what was happening. "It's not a snake, you silly ostrich, it's an umbrella!"

As Ossie opened the umbrella and held it high above his head, a strong breeze blew over the plain and gently lifted the startled ostrich into the air.

"I'm flying," gasped Ossie. "I'm really flying!"

The animals below got such a shock as they looked up and saw an ostrich gliding above the tree tops.

A startled crane flew beside Ossie for a while. "Never thought I'd see an ostrich fly," he called. "I'm off to tell my friends about this."

Ossie the ostrich flew around happily all day and when the wind dropped, he floated gently to the ground.

"That was really exciting!" gasped Ossie as he carefully folded up the umbrella. "I shall carry this wherever I go, and when the wind blows I shall be off on another flying adventure!"

The Big Wooden Toy Box

Tom and Rosie-Anne had a great big toy box. It was made of wood, with a lid that made a very loud bang when you closed it!

The toy box was so large that every single one of Tom and Rosie-Anne's toys fitted inside. This is why the children's room was always so tidy and neat.

Their mother loved the wooden toy box, but the toys did not!

"I don't like being in here one little bit!" said the rag doll to one of the soft toys. "The skipping rope gets tangled round my legs, and I have bricks and jigsaw pieces sticking into my back."

"That sounds very painful," whispered one of the teddies, "but what I hate most of all is the dark, when the lid is closed it's very spooky in here!"

"Perhaps if we all pushed hard we could manage to open the lid," suggested the clown. But the lid was far too heavy, so the toys had to stay in the dark.

One Saturday Tom and Rosie-Anne asked their mother if she had a job for them to do.

"Not at the moment," she said, "but Dad may find you one in the garage."

Dad was delighted and found them a job straight away. "Can you tidy up my tools and put them away in those boxes?"

"What a mess!" cried the children as they looked around the garage. Tools were scattered all over the floor and piled up under benches.

"I wish I had your big wooden toy box!" said their dad with a sigh. "All my tools would fit inside, and when I closed the lid, everything would look tidy."

This gave Tom and Rosie-Anne an idea. "Will you swap all your small tool boxes for our big wooden one?" the children asked.

"I certainly will!" he agreed at once. "We'll do it straight away."

When the job was finished, everyone was happy. Dad had the big wooden toy box with the lid and his garage was never untidy again.

Tom and Rosie-Anne could still keep their room as tidy as ever, and they could see their toys all the time.

As for the toys, they had much more room, they could look around and they were never shut in the dark again.

Fluffy The Tortoise

Grandad had always told Lottie that when the top of her fluffy hat reached the top of the gate she could have a pet!

"Whoopie!" cried Lottie, "I know exactly what I want."

"Come with me to my hen house," said Grandad. "I have a hen with six fluffy chicks. Would you like one of those?"

"They're lovely!" said Lottie, "but I know exactly what I want."

"At the bottom of the garden is a duck with five yellow ducklings. How about one of those?"

"They're great!" said Lottie, "but I know exactly what I want!"

Along came the postwoman with the letters. "I have a cat with three soft kittens. You can choose one of those."

"That's terrific!" said Lottie, "but I know exactly what I want."

Next came the baker bringing the bread. "My dog has four little puppies at home. You can pick one of those if you like."

"How marvellous!" said Lottie, "but I know exactly what I want."

The farmer across the field owned a pony with foals. "Come and take a look, you might like one of those."

" They are beautiful!" said Lottie, "but I know exactly what I want."

In a sty on the farm was a pig with ten little piglets.

"Goodness!" said Lottie. "I couldn't manage even one of those, I know exactly what I want."

Then she went to the pet shop. The man inside said, "Have a good look round before you choose."

"Wonderful!" cried Lottie, "I have found exactly what I want. I want a tortoise!"

Just then a parrot pulled off Lottie's fluffy hat. It dropped right on top of the tortoise.

"Perfect!" cried Lottie, "I shall call you Fluffy the Tortoise. And you are exactly what I want."

39

Hilda The Hippo

Hilda the hippo lived on the bank of a wide muddy river. All the other hippos liked the edge of the river best, where the mud was thick and sticky like warm melted chocolate. They even dozed off to sleep in it on hot afternoons, with the top of their heads just showing above the mud.

"Come on in!" cried the rest of Hilda's family. "The mud is lovely!" But Hilda was not keen on the idea at all, she liked standing in the clean, refreshing rain, especially during a thunderstorm. Best of all she loved to watch the frogs leaping onto the lily-pads and floating on top of the water.

"I wish I could do that," Hilda sighed. "Then I would never get muddy!" But each time Hilda tried to fit all four feet onto a lily-pad, she sank like a stone!

Now frogs can be very helpful creatures and full of good ideas. So one day, they pushed a lily-pad under each one of Hilda's back feet and gave her two long poles to help her along. With a bit of practise, Hilda was soon skiing across the water on her lily-pad skis.

It so happened that one day a photographer took Hilda's picture and sent it to a wildlife magazine. Very soon, everyone wanted to see Hilda, the skiing hippo.

"In my country," the photographer told Hilda, "everyone skis all the time! Why don't you come and see for yourself?"

So Hilda left her muddy river and flew far away on an aeroplane. It was very exciting!

When she landed, the little hippo couldn't believe her eyes. Everywhere was white! Mountains, hills, even streets were covered in thick, fluffy, white snow.

In no time at all, Hilda jumped on a pair of skis and whizzed off down the mountain side. In and out of the trees she sped until she came to an enormous ski jump. Hilda took off, flew through the air, then made a perfect landing at the bottom.

"What a winner!" yelled the crowd. "It's the longest jump ever made!" They gave Hilda a shiny, gold medal.

Hilda stayed a while to ski in the snowy land, and when she returned on the aeroplane, she wore her gold medal around her neck - just to show the frogs on the muddy river back home!

The Mole's Adventure

"What a lovely morning," purred Ginger the cat as he stepped outside the front door. "I think I shall take a stroll round the garden."

So Ginger walked down the path, past the flower bed, then walked back again along the top of the fence.

"That's enough exercise for one morning," said Ginger out loud, and jumped down onto the grass.

All of a sudden, a small mound of earth appeared right next to him. "Goodness me," gasped Ginger, "where did that come from?" From the middle of the earth popped a velvety brown mole.

"Good morning to you!" the Mole said with a grin. "I've just come up from my underground burrow in search of an adventure!"

Ginger jumped back up onto the fence in surprise. "What sort of adventure would you like?" he asked the Mole.

"I want to climb up on the fence just like you," laughed the Mole. "Better still, I would like to climb a tree!"

"Moles can't climb trees," said Ginger with a shake of his head, "but that would be an adventure for you. Just let me think for a minute!"

So Ginger sat on the fence, closed his eyes and thought and thought.

At last he came up with a wonderful idea which he whispered to the Mole.

Behind the fence were two apple trees and on the lowest branch of one was a swing. Ginger helped the Mole up onto the seat and pushed it until he was swinging higher and higher. Then, quick as a wink, Ginger ran up the other tree and grabbed the Mole as he swung near to him.

The two then sat side by side on one of the branches. "Now you have climbed a tree!" laughed Ginger.

"What a great adventure!" gasped the Mole, quite out of breath.

Soon a small crowd gathered under the apple tree. "Look!" they shouted pointing up at the branch, "a Mole that can climb trees!"

How the two new friends laughed. "Perhaps someone will take our picture," said Ginger, "then you will be able to show everyone how you once really did climb a tree!"

Let's Go On A Picnic

One fine, warm summer's day a few of the woodland folk discussed going on a day out.

"It's a perfect day for a picnic," said the fox, as he gazed up at the clear blue sky.

"Why don't we pack a picnic basket and go on a hike?" suggested two chipmunks, who were always very helpful.

Everyone agreed it was a splendid idea, and ran back home to fetch some food.

In next to no time, the animals were back and the picnic basket full to the brim.

"This basket is rather heavy," said a rabbit, as he tried to lift one corner.

"We can take turns carrying it," suggested one of the helpful chipmunks, "we'll take the first turn!"

So the friends set off. They walked through the wood, down a lane, then across a meadow until they came to a stream.

"Look at that lovely place over there, it's just perfect for a picnic," called the porcupine, as he pointed to a field across the water.

"But how are we going to get across?" cried the animals all together.

"Look, a log has fallen across the stream!" cried the two chipmunks, helpful as ever.

"I'll go first," said the fox. "I have a perfect sense of balance."

"Me next," said the porcupine, who couldn't keep his balance at all. "If I slip, I shall fall onto the rabbits!"

"Oh no you won't!" cried the rabbits hopping in front. One by one they crossed the log with great care. How funny the five looked as they wobbled their way along the log trying to keep balance.

Now while all this was going on, the two helpful little chipmunks had been very busy. Believe it or not, the animals' picnic was already set out in the opposite field.

The chipmunks had noticed that the fallen log was hollow. It was quite big enough for them to scamper through and carry all the picnic food to the other side. The rabbits, the porcupine and the fox could have gone through the log quite easily, instead of wobbling their way across!

At last the five friends reached the other side of the stream and flopped down on the grass with relief. And what do you think they found? The two chipmunks sitting by the side of the picnic, helpless with laughter!

Later on when the picnic was over, everybody went back through the hollow log with no trouble at all!

The two little chipmunks led the way, and helpful as ever, carried the empty picnic basket back home.

45

Matilda Is Missing

Matilda went everywhere with Maggie. Matilda was Maggie's favourite doll and when Maggie went out, she took Matilda with her zipped up safely in her own special bag.

One day Maggie went for a walk across the park with Matilda's zip-bag slung over her shoulder.

"How about a swing?" Maggie asked as she unzipped Matilda's special bag.

Poor Maggie gasped! The bag was empty! She yelled at the top of her voice. "Matilda is missing!"

She shouted so loudly that everyone in the park could hear. In fact, Maggie's voice was so noisy, that everyone in the town could hear her too.

Even Maggie's mother could hear her cry, "Matilda is missing!" although she was inside the house.

As fast as possible, Maggie's mother ran upstairs and saw there Matilda the doll sitting on Maggie's bed. She had slipped from the bag and was safe at home all the time.

"What a silly girl I am!" said Maggie when she found out, and her face went very red indeed!

The Lonely Little Lighthouse

In the middle of the sea, perched safely on top of the rocks, stood a little lighthouse. His light shone far out to sea, but no ship had passed by for years. So one day, the lighthouse keeper said goodbye and left him all alone.

This made the little lighthouse feel very sad. "I'm no use to anyone anymore," he sobbed. "My light will soon go out and I'll be forgotten!"

Now some of the seals and walruses who visited the rocks heard the lonely lighthouse. So they put their heads together, and very soon thought of a way to cheer him up.

"We can take it in turns to be the lighthouse keeper and work the light!" suggested the biggest walrus.

The little lighthouse liked the sound of this and began to brighten up right away.

So every night, when darkness falls over the sea, the little lighthouse shines his light. Then the dolphins, the seals and the walruses, sometimes even a couple of whales, come out to play.

Everyone has a wonderful time, especially the little lighthouse. His light shines in the dark like a star and he is never ever lonely.

Jolly Monster's Birthday

It was Jolly Monster's birthday and he was giving a great big birthday party. All his monster friends had been invited and Jolly Monster was hoping for some very large presents, but what he wanted most of all was a big surprise.

That afternoon when the Jolly Monster's friends arrived for tea, each one was carrying a great big box. Jolly Monster could hardly wait to open them.

In the first box was an enormous pair of trainers with red laces.

"I could run a marathon in these!" chuckled Jolly Monster.

When he opened the next box, he found a tee-shirt, not quite the right size!

Most of his friends had brought useful things, like a huge pairs of socks, gigantic gloves, but he received a hat that was far too small!

Some brought games and large balloons that could be seen from far away.

There were sacks full of sweets and lollipops as tall as trees.

All of a sudden someone yelled, "Hide your eyes Jolly Monster, here comes the big surprise!"

Speeding across the lawn came a lorry loaded down with....what do you think?

The biggest blow up castle you have ever seen. Just perfect for Jolly Monster and his friends to bounce up and down on all day!

"I wished for a big surprise, and this is just perfect!" laughed Jolly Monster, as he jumped up into the air.

Bobby Gets Dressed

Little Bobby Briggs was a very good boy, except for one thing. He would not get dressed in the morning!

When the alarm clock rang at eight o'clock, Bobby would jump out of bed straight away, run to the bathroom, wash, clean his teeth and comb his hair but - he would not get dressed in the morning!

This made everyone very cross as well as very late.

One day his sister Susie thought of a good idea. She put all Bobby's clothes for that day into a pillow case and then played his favourite tune on his toy xylophone.

"When the music stops," Susie told her little brother, "take something out of the pillow case and put it on!"

Bobby thought this was a great game and couldn't wait to join in.

First he took out his hat, and when the music stopped again he put on a sock. Next came his sweater, then another sock, then pants and a shirt and very soon he was dressed to go out.

What a good idea sister Susie! Are you going to play this game with Bobby every time he goes out?

51

Racing Rabbit

A postcard came one day for Wise Rabbit. It was from his long lost cousins who lived half way across the world.

'Do come and visit us as soon as you can,' the message read. Wise Rabbit thought this a good idea.

"It's rather a long way," Wise Rabbit said, "but if I can find someone to mow my lawn and look after my garden shed, I shall go at once!"

The neighbours said, "Ask any one of us to mow your lawn and look after your garden shed, but whatever you do, don't ask Bunny Hopkins!"

This made Wise Rabbit think long and hard.

The very next day when Bunny Hopkins passed by, Wise Rabbit gave him the key to the garden shed.

"Leave everything to me!" said Bunny Hopkins eagerly. "I will mow your lawn every week and guard your garden shed with my life."

Off went Wise Rabbit to visit his cousins, but sadly, Bunny Hopkins did not keep his promise.

All summer long he sat in the garden sunbathing. The grass on the lawn grew tall and the weeds almost covered the garden shed.

"I think it's about time I mowed the lawn!" said Bunny Hopkins with a yawn.

When at last the young rabbit unlocked the garden shed, he was in for a big surprise! For standing next to the mower was the biggest motorbike he had ever seen.

On top of the seat was a note which read, 'When you have finished mowing the lawn, use my bike as often as you like.'

Poor Bunny Hopkins just stood and stared. "If I'd mowed the lawn each week as I'd promised, I could have ridden the bike all summer!" he cried.

How quickly Bunny Hopkins got to work, and at last when all the jobs were finished, he raced off on Wise Rabbit's magnificent motorbike.

"Soon Wise Rabbit will be back," sighed Bunny Hopkins, "and I won't be able to ride the motorbike ever again!"

But on the very day he was due to return, Bunny Hopkins received a postcard. It was from Wise Rabbit!

The card was addressed to 'Bunny Hopkins, The Racing Rabbit', and this is what it said: 'I am going to stay here until next year. Please mow my lawn, look after my garden shed and don't forget to ride my motorbike!' Bunny Hopkins was delighted.

Terry's First Prize

Terry drove a yellow taxi all day long. The city streets were very busy with lots of noisy traffic, which often gave Terry a headache. "Sometimes I wish I lived in a place with no cars at all," he sighed.

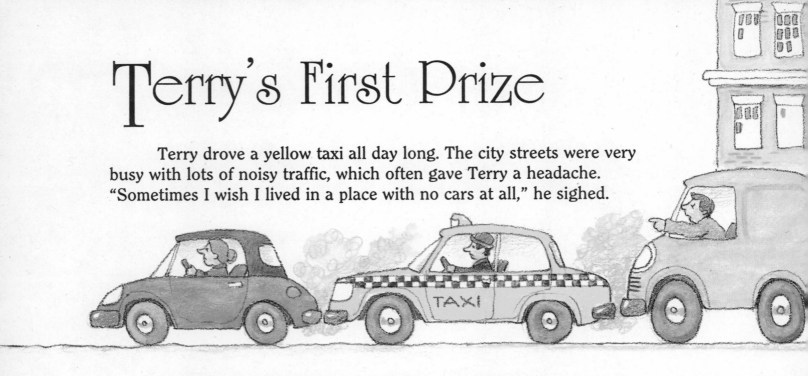

One day a man knocked on Terry's door. "You have won first prize in our great competition!"

Terry looked pleased. "Is it a desert island?" he asked the man.

"I'll give you a clue!" the man smiled. "It has four wheels and travels on the road."

Terry's face fell. "I hope it's not a car!" he cried. He soon cheered up when he saw his very own gipsy caravan!

Mrs Bruno's Pies

Mrs Bruno baked marvellous hot cherry pies. They tasted so good that everyone wanted to buy them. Before long Mrs Bruno's hot cherry pies became famous.

"What am I going to do?" asked Mrs Bruno, looking worried. "I love to bake cherry pies, but when I stop to answer the door, the pies in the oven get burnt, and I have so far to walk to my customers, that my pies are cold by the time they are delivered."

What a problem!

"I think I shall have to stop baking my hot cherry pies!"

"What! No more pies?" cried the customers. So they got together and came up with a splendid idea. They would come and collect the pies from Mrs Bruno's house.

Now Mrs Bruno can bake her famous hot cherry pies, and everyone is happy!

The Musical Mouse

Morgan the mouse made no noise at all. "You really are as quiet as a mouse Morgan!" everyone said with a smile.

"Mice are naturally quiet creatures," nodded Morgan wisely. Then he scampered off without so much as a rustle or a squeak.

Now one day, as Morgan was sitting perfectly still by the side of the road, he heard a wonderful sound. As he listened the sound grew louder and louder.

"It's coming nearer!" shouted Morgan at the top of his voice, which was very unlike him.

Just then the town band came round the corner playing catchy tunes on their instruments.

Morgan had never heard music before and knew he had to join in.

"I've been so quiet all my life," yelled Morgan as he ran alongside the players, "I want to make a great big noise!"

"Try these cymbals," said the cat. Morgan crashed them together so hard that the band almost fell over one another.

"Try this trombone," suggested the dog. Morgan played so hard he almost blew the band away.

Next he tried the drums and made such a noise that the elephants ran behind a wall in fright.

"I thought mice were supposed to be quiet creatures!" whispered one of the band.

"We are!" Morgan agreed as he banged hard on a tambourine, "but making a noise is such wonderful fun!"

By now the band was in a muddle. They were playing different tunes and everyone was bumping into each other.

Suddenly the band leader shouted above the din. "You can be leader of the band Morgan, then everybody can get back to making music instead of a noise!"

Honey Bear's Promise

Honey Bear was very fond of sweet things to eat. He loved jam and candy bars, sticky gingerbread and sugary biscuits - but most of all he loved honey! Every morning, he spread it thickly on hot toast. At lunch time he let it trickle all over his pancakes, and at tea he gobbled up a huge plateful of tasty honey sandwiches.

Now Mother Bear kept the honey on the very top shelf of the kitchen cupboard. The shelf was far too high for Honey Bear to reach unless he climbed to the top of Father's wooden steps.

One day, when he thought no-one was looking, Honey Bear carried Father's wooden steps into the kitchen.

"If I'm very quiet and ever so careful, I can climb up and reach the honey jar from the top shelf," Honey Bear chuckled to himself. But when Honey Bear got almost to the top, the steps began to wobble and shake which gave the little bear quite a fright.

"Help! Help!" yelled Honey Bear as he clung onto the steps.

Luckily, Father Bear was behind the kitchen door and caught Honey Bear before he fell off and hurt himself.

Father Bear looked very cross."You must promise never to climb the steps," he said sternly, "it's far too dangerous!"

Honey Bear hung his head and promised.

The very next day when Honey Bear looked longingly at that big jar of honey, he remembered his promise. Then all of a sudden he had a wonderful idea. "I know how to reach the honey, without using Father's steps at all!"

So very carefully he opened the bottom drawer of the cupboard, then the next drawer, and the next, and so on, until he could reach that tempting jar of honey.

Honey Bear slowly climbed down with the precious jar tucked safely in his paw. He reached for a spoon from the top drawer of the cupboard, then settled down to enjoy the lovely honey!

The Runaround Clock

The alarm clock on the bedroom shelf opened his eyes and looked around. Dawn was breaking and the first rays of the sun were just peeping through the curtains.

"I'm bored!" the clock ticked. "Everyone is still fast asleep. I've been ticking away all through the night, and no-one has listened to a single tic-toc!"

"That's what clocks are supposed to do!" snapped a china dog on the shelf, "just tic-toc away all night and all day."

"Well, it's very boring!" replied the alarm clock crossly. "No-one listens to me until eight o'clock when my alarm bell rings!"

The alarm clock looked down at his hands. "It's only five o'clock. I think I shall go for a run." And with that he jumped off the shelf and ran downstairs.

Once outside, the alarm clock dashed off quickly down the street. He hadn't gone very far when a small dog, out for his early morning walk, barked and growled at the poor alarm clock. The dog chased him across the road, where a boy delivering newspapers almost ran over him with his bicycle wheel.

Then, without any warning, a machine that cleans the street, sprayed him with cold water and whisked him along the gutter with its whurring brushes.

"Oh dear me!" gasped the alarm clock, looking down at his hands. "It's six o'clock. I've only been outside an hour. How I wish I was back on the shelf at home."

But there was worse to come! The man who drove the dustcart saw the alarm clock upside down in the gutter. He thought it was a piece of junk and threw him onto his cart!

The dustcart travelled round the streets for ages collecting more and more rubbish. At last the alarm clock struggled to the top of the pile and peered out of the back of the cart.

To his great delight he was only two doors away from his own house, so he jumped down from the cart and rolled into his very own garden.

The cat, who had been out all night, sniffed at the alarm clock, then pushed him over with her paw.

"Look at the time!" gasped the alarm clock as he looked at his hands. "It's almost five minutes to eight!"

With one last effort he ran upstairs, jumped back on bedroom shelf and rang his bell as hard as he could.

"Time to get up!" cried one of the family. "It's exactly eight o'clock and our alarm clock is right on time as usual!"

Who Has Eaten The Garden?

In spring (when the weather begins to turn warm), Lottie and Grandma spent hours planting vegetable seeds in the garden.

Lottie thought they took ages to grow, but one morning in summer Grandma said that at last they were ready for picking.

"Let's have peas today!" said Lottie. "They're my favourite!"

So she took a bowl into the garden and filled it with fresh green pea-pods. Then she sat outside the kitchen door and shelled the peas for lunch - perhaps she ate one or two as well!

The next day Lottie chose carrots for lunch, but when she went out to pick them, she found that something had been nibbling the garden. Most of the vegetables had been eaten! Whatever could it be?

"It must be rabbits!" said the milkman. "They love carrots."

"It can't be," said Lottie. "I give them plenty of lettuce and cabbage leaves!"

"It must be pigeons!" said the postman. "They love peas."

"Never!" cried Lottie. "I give them corn and crumbs all the time."

"Then, it's slugs!" said the boy returning from school. "They'll eat anything."

"Oh dear!" sighed Lottie. "What shall we do?"

"Make a scarecrow," suggested Grandad. "We'll do it this afternoon."

Next morning, as soon as it was light, Lottie crept downstairs and tiptoed into the vegetable garden. What a surprise she got! Not rabbits, not pigeons or even slugs - but a baby deer nibbling beans and making friends with the scarecrow.

Very quietly, Lottie crept up to the deer and stroked his nose. "So it was you who ate the garden," she whispered. "I wish I could keep you as a pet."

Grandad shook his head. "I'm sure if you put out some food, the little deer will come out of the wood to see you sometimes," he said with a smile. "As long as he leaves our vegetables alone!"

The Animal Olympics

Once a year the animals held a meeting. They talked about this and that, told one another all their news, then everyone joined in a gigantic party.

Now this year they wanted to do something quite different, so they decided to hold the Animal Olympics!

"We'll all meet back here one week from now," suggested the elephant. "Then everyone can take part and try to win a gold medal."

"How exciting!" cried all the animals, and they ran off at once to practise.

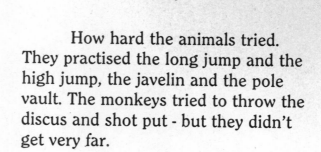

How hard the animals tried. They practised the long jump and the high jump, the javelin and the pole vault. The monkeys tried to throw the discus and shot put - but they didn't get very far.

"I'm the fastest animal in the world," sobbed Cheetah. "If I take part I shall win all the races, and it will be no fun at all!"

"Cheer up!" said the Hippo. "I have the perfect job for a fast runner like you. Will you carry the Olympic torch and start the games?"

The cheetah was delighted and stopped crying at once.

The day of the Animal Olympic Games came at last. The animals arrived looking very smart in their sports clothes, all except one. Tommy Tortoise stood on his own looking very sad. "I've practised everyday, but I'm far too slow to take part in any event," he sobbed.

"Not to worry!" said the Hippo. "We need someone to fire the starting pistol and time the races."

Tommy Tortoise cheered up at once and plodded off to the starting point.

All of a sudden, one of the other animals began sniffing. It was the cheetah.

"Why are you crying too?" asked the Hippo rather surprised.

At last the Animal Olympics began. They lasted all day long, and each animal won a medal for one event or another.

Everyone went home late that evening feeling very happy and very tired - especially the tortoise and the cheetah!

The Rocky Mountain Train

Once upon a time there was a Red Train which carried people across the Rocky Mountains.

Everyday the Red Train had to pull lots of carriages, because so many people wanted to cross the mountains to the other side. Slowly, the Red Train huffed and puffed his way over the mountains with his load getting heavier and heavier everyday.

"My goodness!" said the engine driver, when he saw more and more

In the rain and frost and snow.
The bright Red Train will be our guide,
Until we reach the other side.
Merrily he'll puff along,
Until we end this happy song!"

One morning, there were even more people than usual waiting at the station. Very soon the Red Train's carriages were packed full of passengers.

The Red Train pulled very

people waiting at the station each morning. "If I add any more carriages, the Red Train will break down one day!"

Now the Red Train kept going because he liked to make the passengers happy, and he loved to listen to the song they sang on the journey across the Rocky Mountains.

"Through the mountain we will go,

slowly out of the station, but as soon as he started to cross the mountains, he huffed and puffed, blew his whistle and came to a stop.

"Poor Red Train," said his engine driver. "He's too tired to go any further!"

"Oh dear!" cried all the passengers. "This is our fault. What can we do?"

All of a sudden a little boy jumped down from the train and shouted to the passengers leaning out of the carriage windows.

"The song we always sing says '*through* the mountains we will go', perhaps the Red Train used to go through the mountains and there is a hidden tunnel somewhere - that would

save going up and over them!"

The Red Train blew his whistle very hard, he could just remember going through the tunnel many years ago.

At once the passengers climbed out of the train, they searched round the mountain until at last they found the opening of the old tunnel.

Everyone worked very hard pulling away tangled undergrowth and clearing the track.

Very soon the Red Train was speeding happily through the tunnel, straight through the mountains in next to no time. The passengers sang the Red Train's very own song at the tops of their voices!

Jed's Special Sweater

One afternoon Jed's great aunt Jenny came to his house for tea. Jed liked his great aunt Jenny because she was kind and funny, and had a very special wrist watch that played 'Happy Birthday' even if it wasn't your birthday that day!

After tea, Great Aunt Jenny asked Jed if she could borrow a book about space travel. Jed had lots, so he gave her a book full of pictures of spacemen, rockets and the moon.

Next time Great Aunt Jenny came to tea she was carrying a brown paper parcel.

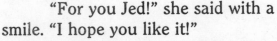

"For you Jed!" she said with a smile. "I hope you like it!"

Inside the parcel Jed found a lovely bright red sweater. On the front Great Aunt Jenny had carefully knitted a picture of a spaceman in his helmet, with a silver rocket in the background.

"Just like the picture in your book," laughed Great Aunt Jenny as Jed pulled on his wonderful sweater.

He was delighted with his present and wanted to wear it everyday. He tried very hard not to get it dirty, because he missed his sweater so much when it had to be washed.

Every Thursday Jed and his school friends went to the swimming pool with their teacher. After the swimming lesson, all the children rushed into the changing rooms to get dried and dressed.

"Quick as you can, children!" called their teacher. "The bus is waiting to take you back to school."

Quickly Jed pulled on his clothes, tied his shoes, then hunted round for his special sweater. At last he spotted it under a bench on the wet floor. Fast as he could, Jed tugged on his sweater, then hurried onto the bus with all the others.

Later that afternoon, as Jed was walking home, he looked down at his sweater and got quite a shock. The front was plain red and the spacemen with his rocket had vanished.

"Oh no!" gasped poor Jed, almost in tears. "I must have put on the wrong sweater!"

When he got home Great Aunt Jenny was there. "I've lost my spaceman sweater," sobbed Jed.

All of a sudden Great Aunt Jenny began to smile and Jed's mother laughed out loud.

"Your sweater's back to front," giggled Great Aunt Jenny. "Come here, you silly boy," and she turned Jed's sweater around, so the spaceman and the rocket were at the front for everyone to see!

Teddy's Soup

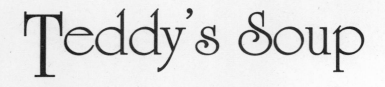

Teddy Bear had a problem, he was very bad at spelling.

"I do try really hard!" he told Mother Bear. "In fact, I am busy reading my book right now."

Mother Bear smiled to herself when she noticed that Teddy was holding his book upside down.

Then she thought of a bright idea. Mother Bear went into the kitchen straight away and made Teddy a large bowl of alphabet soup.

"Now you can learn your letters as you eat," she laughed.

The alphabet tasted so good, that Teddy emptied the bowl in one gulp.

"Perhaps that wasn't such a good idea after all," chuckled Mother Bear, as she filled Teddy's bowl up with soup once more!

Cathy's Tea Party

One afternoon, deep down at the bottom of the ocean, Cathy the crab was giving a tea party.

That morning she had made lots of iced buns, a very fancy cake and two huge plates of seaweed sandwiches.

In the afternoon when she laid the table, Cathy set out eight plates and eight cups and saucers.

"How many guests are coming to the tea party?" asked a cheeky little fish passing by.

"I've invited one guest," giggled Cathy. "It's Ollie the Octopus!"

"I need a plate for each of my eight arms," laughed Ollie as he put a delicious cake onto each plate.

Mike The Mixer

Mike the mixer was brand new. His orange paintwork gleamed, his mixer was spotless, even his tyres were perfectly clean.

It was Mike the mixer's first day out and he was longing to get dirty. "I hope lots of people will want cement," he said to himself, as he drove along the road to find some work.

He hadn't travelled very far before he came to some major roadworks. On the left was a long queue of trucks and lorries waiting to dump their loads.

"Have you brought any stone or tarmac to put on the roads?" shouted the man in charge.

"Nothing at all," replied Mike, "but I'll fetch you a load of cement."

"Don't bother," said the man. "We don't need any here. Now get out of the way!"

So Mike the mixer hurried on until he came to a building site. "This looks promising," he said to himself, as he parked beside a pile of bricks and some sand.

"Can I fetch you a load of cement?" Mike called to a bricklayer building a wall.

"Too late," yelled the man. "We've almost finished for today. Can you move, you're blocking the way?"

Quickly Mike drove on and turned down the next road where he found a man laying a new path in his garden.

When he saw Mike, the man shouted across, "I've just mixed all this concrete myself and now I've got blisters and backache. You should have come an hour ago!"

"Oh dear!" thought Mike as he drove on. "I won't find any work there."

All the next week Mike tried to find something to do, but nobody wanted a load of cement.

Mike was feeling very sorry for himself, so he drove around until he found a quiet street. He gave a deep sigh and switched off his engine.

At that very moment, Mike heard a loud voice right beside him. "You're just what I need. A cement mixer is the answer to all my problems!" A very excited baker was standing next to him, for Mike had parked right outside his shop.

"Today I must bake the tallest birthday cake in the world," the busy baker explained. "I don't have a bowl big enough to mix the cake and my poor arms will ache with all that stirring. Will you help me out?"

Mike the cement mixer was thrilled - a job at last!

The busy baker got to work at once. He loaded butter, sugar, flour and dried fruit into Mike's mixer. Then he tossed in one hundred eggs and a whole box of spices.

Mike started his engine and his mixer began to turn. The busy baker shouted, "Whoa!" when he thought everything was ready. Then Mike tilted his mixer and poured the cake-mix into eleven giant cake tins.

The cakes took hours to bake. When they were ready and had cooled, the baker decorated them with pink sugar icing, while Mike watched through the shop door.

"Who ordered such a giant cake?" Mike asked the baker that night.

"I've no idea!" replied the busy baker, shaking his head. "We shall find out tomorrow."

And find out they did! Next morning the zoo keeper arrived with some of his staff to take the giant cake back with them to the zoo.

"Today is our giraffe's birthday and we wanted a cake as tall as him!"

The baker and Mike were invited to the zoo and asked to join the party.

"Could you stay and work for me and mix cakes instead of cement?" the baker asked Mike.

Mike the cake mixer agreed at once!

75

The Counting Caterpillar

Some caterpillars like to munch leaves and stalks all day, while others nibble fruit and flowers.

Colin the caterpillar was different. He loved to count!

To begin with, he counted from one to ten. It wasn't long before he could count up to a hundred.

As Colin crawled slowly along he counted the world around him...one bud on a rose, two wings on a wasp, three bugs in a jar, four wings on a dragonfly, five grubs in a peach, six legs on a cricket, seven stripes on a beetle, eight legs on a spider, nine leaves on a plant and ten petals on a daisy.

Colin counted all day long. He counted the insects buzzing around him and the ants as they marched through the long grass.

First thing every morning as Colin was busy counting, a bright red ladybird and her family passed by on their way to the rose garden. Mother ladybird had six black spots, each baby had two.

"Good morning," called Colin counting out loud. "Sixteen spots, twelve feelers, thirty-six legs, have a nice day!"

Then Colin crawled off and spent the rest of that day counting the seeds in a giant sunflower. When all the ladybirds returned later that day,

things did not add up. Colin was puzzled. Quickly he counted fourteen spots, ten feelers, and only thirty legs. Something was wrong!

One young ladybird had been left behind, but was soon found upside-down in a rose petal.

"Everyone should learn to count!" said Mother Ladybird as she thanked Colin. "It's very useful."

"I agree!" nodded Colin wisely. "Tomorrow I shall count up to 1,000!"

The Pumpkin Man

One day in spring Joe the gardener planted some seeds in his vegetable plot. Joe's cat and dog and even his white rabbit lent a hand.

"When the autumn comes," said Joe, "we shall have plenty of pumpkins!"

Joe was absolutely right. At harvest time his garden was full of ripe orange pumpkins of every shape and size.

Joe, his cat and dog and even his white rabbit had never seen so many pumpkins.

"I shall pick the biggest one," said Joe proudly, "and we shall have pumpkin pie every day."

"Ugh!" groaned Joe's cat and dog and even his rabbit, because they hated the stuff!

So all that day Joe baked pumpkin pies. He cooked so many they filled the kitchen, but still he had only used up half his biggest pumpkin.

"Time to eat," shouted Joe, as he cut for the cat and dog, and even the white rabbit, a huge slice of pumpkin pie.

"But we hate pumpkin pie!" cried the cat, the dog and even the rabbit.

"And so do I," agreed Joe, when he took his first bite.

"So what can we do with all these pumpkins?" the four friends shouted together.

It was the white rabbit who thought of the best idea.

"Tomorrow is Halloween," he told the others, "everyone will need lots and lots of pumpkins."

So this is what they did.

The rest of that day, Joe and his cat, dog and rabbit, cut and carved the pumpkins ready for Halloween.

When darkness fell, they put a candle in every pumpkin shell and hung them outside the house and all over the garden.

What a beautiful sight hundreds of golden lanterns made with their bright lights flickering in the darkness.

Very soon a huge crowd gathered outside Joe's house. People saw the glowing pumpkin lamps as they passed, and everyone wanted to buy one to take home.

By midnight all the pumpkins had been sold and everyone was happy.

"I love Halloween," sighed the white rabbit, "but best of all I love the pumpkin lanterns."

"Oh my goodness," gasped Joe to his cat and dog. "I'm afraid we've sold the last one."

So the next day, on Halloween, they had to go out and buy a pumpkin - just for the white rabbit.

The Little Red Helicopter

Right on the edge of a busy airport stood the Little Red Helicopter.
All day long he watched the huge jet planes taking off and landing
on the runway, as they carried passengers to far away places.

"It must be wonderful taking people on holiday," sighed the Little
Red Helicopter, "but nobody ever notices me!"

Every morning the Little Red Helicopter flew businessmen into the
city to work and brought them back to the same place every night.

It was very dull. No-one ever smiled at the Little Red Helicopter or
thanked him for a nice flight. His passengers ignored him, they were far
too busy to notice the Little Red Helicopter.

Now one morning something different happened. A worried
looking gentleman came running towards the Little Red Helicopter.

"Can you take off and land in a a very small place?" the
gentleman shouted loudly. "Will you please come to our rescue?"

The Little Red Helicopter was overjoyed. Adventure at last! He
agreed at once.

Straight away, the staff from the airport pulled out the Little
Red Helicopter's seats and began to fill up the space with sacks and
bales of hay. How they scratched and tickled the poor Little Red
Helicopter.

The pilot climbed in and started the engine, the blades began to spin and soon they were flying high over the airport.

"We must travel across country and up into the hills!" shouted the pilot above all the noise. "Do you think you can land with such a heavy load?"

"I think I can," whirred the Little Red Helicopter. "I'll do my very best."

When he reached the hills the Little Red Helicopter looked down. There were floods everywhere! The countryside below him was covered with water and the animals had been moved to higher ground,

At last the Little Red Helicopter reached the hillside and landed carefully on a very small space.

Everyone clapped and cheered and shouted, "Well done!" They crowded round the Little Red Helicopter and made him feel like a hero.

The animals hadn't eaten for two whole days. Soon they were tucking into the food that the Little Red Helicopter had brought such a long way.

"You've saved the day," said the pilot with a smile. "Would you like to be a rescue helicopter from now on?"

The Little Red Helicopter lifted right off the ground with pride. The very next day the pilot painted the words 'Rescue Helicopter' in black on his side.

The Clowns' Breakfast

Three funny circus clowns lived together in one house. One clown washed the clothes, one clown cooked the meals and the other clown kept the house neat and tidy. Most of the time they got on very well, but there was one thing that they could not agree upon.

Every morning before they went to work at the circus, the three funny clowns would have breakfast together.

They all drank fresh coffee with cream and sugar. They all ate hot toast with butter and jam, but most of all they enjoyed boiled eggs in their very own egg cups.

Each morning the three funny clowns sat round the table listening to their eggs as they bubbled in the pan. After exactly four minutes the eggs were ready...and that was when the trouble began!

"That's my egg, put it down!"

"Mine was white, yours is brown!"

"They're just the same, put my egg back!"

"Don't mix them up, they're sure to crack!"

The three funny clowns could never agree which egg was which. That was a pity because their eggs got cold, their toast was burnt and their coffee tasted terrible.

Breakfast was spoiled every day!

"This is no way for three clowns to behave," said the three friends as they gazed at each other sadly.

Suddenly one of the clowns jumped up. "All this fuss over three boiled eggs," he cried, as he pulled a pencil from a pocket in his big baggy trousers. "I have the answer to our problem!"

He picked up one of the eggs and drew a clown's face on it, exactly like his own. Then the other two clowns did the same.

Now, every morning, each clown draws his own face on his egg before popping it into the pan.

When the eggs are ready there are no more problems, just three happy, hungry clowns.

Sam The Scribbling Snake

One day as Sam the Snake slithered along the floor of the steamy jungle, he found a big box of sharp, shiny pencils.

"Ssssuper," hissed Sam. "What a simply smashing surprise!" With that, he picked up a pencil and began to scribble.

First he scribbled in the sand, then he scribbled on the flowers and leaves. Next he scribbled up and down the tree trunks. He even scribbled all over the animals.

Something had to be done!

"Sam has lots of pencils," said the baby elephant, "we must find him lots of paper to scribble on!"

Before very long, the animals came back with notebooks and pads of every shape and size and sheets and sheets of paper.

"Stupendous!" Sam hissed happily. "I'll start slowly by spelling short sentences. Soon I shall scribble short stories about all my friends in the jungle."

Sam scribbled so many stories that some were made into books and films, and very soon Sam the Scribbling Snake became a Superstar!

The Sound Asleep Pig

Patti the pig could not get up in the morning. The bell on her alarm clock rang loudly at seven o'clock, but Patti didn't hear a thing.

At eight o'clock, the rooster from the farmyard perched on top of her bed and crowed as loud as he could for half an hour. Still Patti the pig did not wake up!

"I'll try too!" said the owl, and he hooted from nine until ten. Then he flew home to sleep for the day.

Will nothing wake Patti the pig?

At eleven o'clock, the old grey donkey stuck his head through her bedroom window. He brayed loudly in Patti's ear, until everybody begged him to stop.

How can Patti the pig sleep through all that noise - will she never wake up?

At twelve o'clock the farmer's wife said, "I know how to wake her up!"

She opened Patti's door and shouted, "Dinner time!" In a flash Patti was awake and ready for her dinner.

Now we all know how to wake Patti the sound asleep pig!

85

Dolly's Telephone

One morning as Dolly was looking in her mirror she gave a little scream. Her face was covered in spots!

"Oh dear! Oh dear!" said the doctor, shaking his head. "You must stay in bed for a whole week."

"But I don't feel in the least bit ill," wailed Dolly, and she went to bed and sulked.

The other toys tried to cheer her up. They came round to visit her. They brought books and games and flowers and chocolates, which they left outside her bedroom door.

"I shall have no-one to talk to for a whole week!" snapped Dolly, and she pulled the bedclothes over her head.

All the toys felt sorry for Dolly, but they didn't want to go near her just in case they caught the spots too.

"I think I know how to help," piped up a tinkling little voice.

It was the toy telephone. "I will go to visit Dolly this afternoon. She can talk to her friends for an hour and that will cheer her up!"

Dolly was thrilled to see the toy telephone and began to dial straight away. "I have dolly friends all over the world," said Dolly proudly. "Now I can phone every one of them!"

"Oh dear," sighed the toy telephone. "It looks as if I shall be here all week!"

Buzz Builds A Snowman

One winter's day, when the snow lay deep in the garden, William asked his friend, Buzz the Robot, if he would like to make a snowman.

"I don't know how! I don't know how!" whirred Buzz.

"Watch me!" laughed William. "It's very easy!"

So William set to work shovelling the soft snow and piling it up high. He shaped the snow very carefully until he had made a perfect snowman.

"All he needs now is a scarf, some gloves and a hat," smiled William as he stepped back to admire his work. "Now you try Buzz!"

The little robot stared at William's snowman, and all his lights flashed on and off. "Not like that! Not like that!" he cried in his funny robot voice.

He whizzed into the house and came back with a bowl of fruit! This made William howl with laughter.

All of a sudden Buzz whirled his robot arms and there was his snowman made in a flash.

"Looks just like me! Looks just like me!" Buzz giggled, as he pointed to his snowman.

"The bowl of fruit was a great idea," said William. "Only a robot could think of that!"

The Flying Fieldmice

Tim and Tilly Fieldmouse were sitting in a cornfield gazing up at the bright blue sky. As they watched the clouds floating by, Tilly spotted something.

Flying high above them was a helicopter. As it came nearer, Tim spotted something else. "Look!" he squeaked, pointing up into the sky, "someone has jumped out!"

Tim and Tilly Fieldmouse held their breath, then all of a sudden a parachute opened up and a man floated gently to the ground.

"I wish we could ride in a helicopter and go parachuting," said Tilly, with a sigh, "but we're far too small!"

When Tilly looked round Tim was gone. He had scampered up to the top of a hill where a tall sycamore tree grew. Underneath the tree, the ground was covered with sycamore seeds - just like tiny wings.

"Look at me Tilly!" cried Tim, as he jumped into the air. "Have you ever seen a flying fieldmouse before?"

What fun both little mice had. They flew around all afternoon, until they were tired out.

"Let's go flying again tomorrow," laughed Tilly, as the two fieldmice went home to bed.

The Monster On The Moon

There were once two little squirrels who lived high up in an old oak tree.

On dark nights, the thing they liked to do most, was to watch the moon from their bedroom window.

"Is there really a Man in the Moon?" they asked Father Squirrel time after time.

So one night he brought his big, brass telescope up to the squirrels' bedroom. "See for yourself!" smiled Father Squirrel as he pointed the telescope up at the dark night sky.

Both little squirrels stood on their tiptoes and took it in turns to look at the moon through the big brass telescope.

"Can you see the Man in the Moon yet?" joked their Father.

All of a sudden, the two little squirrels let go of the telescope and hid under their bed.

"There's a huge monster on the moon with great big staring eyes!" they shouted with fright.

Father Squirrel leaned out of the bedroom window and started to laugh. "It's only Ollie the Owl perched on a branch. He doesn't look much like the Monster on the Moon to me!"

Goodnight Everybody

Mrs Hedgehog had such a large family it took simply ages for her ten children to get ready for bed.

When all the little hedgehogs had been bathed, they sat together in front of a warm fire with milk and biscuits. The very last thing they did before they went to bed, was brush their teeth and comb their bristly spines. All this took a very long time!

At last, when they were all tucked up in bed and Baby Hedgehog was settled down in his wooden cot, Mrs Hedgehog would say goodnight to every one of her ten children.

Ten children, ten goodnights, what a long job! Then all the children would say goodnight to Mrs Hedgehog, and then say goodnight to each other!

Some nights, they would forget Baby Hedgehog, so they had to begin all over again!

"I shall never get my children to sleep," Mrs Hedgehog would sometimes sigh. However, she usually did, although it was often very late.

One night when all the little hedgehogs were fast asleep, Oswald Owl flew into a tree nearby and began to hoot very loudly. All the little hedgehogs woke up at once, got out of their beds and began to play.

"My goodness," exclaimed Mrs Hedgehog when she heard the noise, "whatever shall I do?"

Poor Mrs Hedgehog. This started to happen every night as soon as the ten young hedgehogs fell fast asleep.

"If I knew what time the children went to bed," hooted Oswald, "I could go and hoot in some other part of the wood!"

This gave Mrs Hedgehog an idea. She searched in one of her cupboards and found a large watch.

So, the very next night, she gave it to Oswald the Owl. "You can hoot up to eight o'clock, not a minute longer!"

Oswald was very pleased indeed with his new watch. He hooted every night on a tree nearby while the hedgehog children got ready for bed. They all said goodnight to each other and settled down. Oswald then looked at his watch, hooted goodnight, then flew away.

"Goodnight everybody, goodnight!"